MARTIAL 'ART'

MARTIAL 'ART'

S.B. DOW

Kroshka Books
New York

Senior Editors: Susan Boriotti and Donna Dennis
Coordinating Editor: Tatiana Shohov
Office Manager: Annette Hellinger
Graphics: Wanda Serrano
Book Production: Matthew Kozlowski, Jonathan Rose and Jennifer Vogt
Circulation: Cathy DeGregory, Ave Maria Gonzalez
Communications and Acquisitions: Serge P. Shohov

Library of Congress Cataloging-in-Publication Data

ISBN 1-56072-486-2

Copyright © 2002 by S.B. Dow
Kroshka Books, a division of
227 Main Street, Suite 100
Huntington, New York 11743
Tele. 631-424-6682   Fax 631-424-4666
e-mail: Novascience@earthlink.net
Web Site: http://www.novapublishers.com

All rights reserved. No part of this book may be reproduced, stored in a retrieval system or transmitted in any form or by any means: electronic, electrostatic, magnetic, tape, mechanical photocopying, recording or otherwise without permission from the publishers.

The authors and publisher have taken care in preparation of this book, but make no expressed or implied warranty of any kind and assume no responsibility for any errors or omissions. No liability is assumed for incidental or consequential damages in connection with or arising out of information contained in this book.

This publication is designed to provide accurate and authoritative information with regard to the subject matter covered herein. It is sold with the clear understanding that the publisher is not engaged in rendering legal or any other professional services. If legal or any other expert assistance is required, the services of a competent person should be sought. FROM A DECLARATION OF PARTICIPANTS JOINTLY ADOPTED BY A COMMITTEE OF THE AMERICAN BAR ASSOCIATION AND A COMMITTEE OF PUBLISHERS.

Printed in the United States of America

To my best friend, Pat, without whose constant belief, support and inspiration, this collection would not have been made possible...

and to my dojo mates - whose tireless effort to achieve perfection provide me with limitless material.

PREFACE

I have been associated with the Martial Arts for nearly half my life, and my efforts have rewarded me with the distinction of holding black belt status in a variety of styles. I have achieved instructor certification through the Ministry of Education in Japan and am currently a board member with the Martial Artists Against Violence (MAAV) Organization.

This collection of cartoons was born from witnessing the frustration in others and myself as we went about the task of trying to perfect ourselves in the art. At times it seemed as though body and mind were not on speaking terms. We could not perform even the simplest of moves without stumbling about. To help ease the growing frustrations at the ineptness we all felt I began highlighting these strays from the norm in a pictorial fashion each week. These drawings served to illustrate that we are not alone in our human shortcomings and that it is all right to flounder from time to time. The main lesson to be learned here is that you have to be able to laugh at yourself if you ever want to truly succeed at anything.

It is important to understand that I take my Martial Arts studies and teaching very seriously. It is also important to note that these depictions are not meant to insult anyone or anything. They were meant to bring a smile to people who study the Arts, and who also understand how difficult it is to meld mind, body and spirit without looking like one of the stooges. It is also designed for those who have no real understanding about the Arts by illustrating that we are all just ordinary men, women, and children with moments of graceless flow. And, if you look closely enough, our efforts are no different than the efforts of those who participate in any other sport ...

I hope you enjoy viewing them as much as I did creating them.

Martial 'Art'

"First, grab the attacker's knife hand with your left hand, then..."

"Oh sure! Live with me! The wolf'll never get through bricks!"

Martial 'Art'

"This is a loaner, mine's in the shop..."

"I'm not usually influenced by a dog or owner, but in this case"

Martial 'Art'

"I can't kick dressed like this. Could you wait here while I go and change?"

"You're getting too much height in your jumps!"

Martial 'Art'

"Hey! When I do that technique you're supposed to let go or it won't work!!"

"Tell me, just how good of a black belt are you?"

"Relax, it's not your floor creaking, it's your students."

"I said I *studied* karate, I didn't say I was any good at it."

Martial 'Art'

"Our guests will be showing us techniques they must have learned from the masters!"

"I need to check my karate manual to find the best way to disarm you..."

"Springs, the latest in pushup technology!"

"It's my anti-theft device!"

"Do the flying leap again, but this time, one student at a time!"

Martial 'Art'

"No, this isn't part of the test, but he doesn't know that!"

"New power saw, work chop-chop"

Martial 'Art'

"Mommy? why is Santa Claus wearing a sword?"

"Working out by candlelight sounded like fun until he melted one onto my head"

"Maybe that kung-fu obedience school was a mistake."

"We don't have a ball to drop at midnight so we'll make do..."

Martial 'Art'

"Complaints are down 99% since he took over!"

"Get out here genie and take care of this guy like I wished!"

Martial 'Art'

"Unbelievable! He bored that robber into submission!"

"Really officer those weapons in my sleigh are gifts for a karate school!"

"Don't go hiding behind me! Get out there and fight!"

"Show me in the rules where this is illegal!"

Martial 'Art'

"Stop the fight! They're knocking the stuffing out of each other!"

"You sure this is how the fish block is done?"

"Karate has taught me confidence, so I'm confident he's going to kill me!"

"Getting my belt knot to touch the floor is easy, it's my arms that's hard!"

Martial 'Art'

"We need to learn karate to protect ourselves from our kids who take it!"

"When you attack, keep your mouth closed!"

Martial 'Art'

"Now THIS is going to be a challenge!"

teaching an old dog new tricks...

"Some martial artist! He jumps up and knocks himself out on the lamp!"

"You have great form, fantastic stance and powerful punches..."

Martial 'Art'

"I don't think your pet tiger needs karate to protect himself..."

"How many know Zenshin Kotai renketsu doza ichi ban?"

"Know it! I can't even say it!"

"Next time I'm studying weapons at the secretarial school..."

"I think these birds'll be too tough to cook..."

Martial 'Art'

"Send a case of sake and some pizzas then they'll release me!!"

"Him? He teaches beginner weapons."

Martial 'Art'

"They're husband and wife. They always spar like that!"

"He won that trophy while running around trying to get a bee out of his uniform!"

"Kiss? Kiss? I thought you said you kick whoever's under the mistletoe!"

"I don't have the time to be robbed today. How about we try Tuesday at 6 PM?"

Martial 'Art'

"Sorry, we teach martial arts here not marshall arts."

"I like the idea of the blindfolds, it's the swords I don't like!"

"Maybe you've been teaching the kids' classes too long..."

HOW TOURNAMENT SCORES ARE REALLY CALCULATED...

"Judge #3, your score will be..."

Martial 'Art'

"Just get ready to fight and stop looking up every word I say!"

"This way I save the cost of a ladder, and you get stronger legs..."

Martial 'Art'

"Maybe those aren't weapons they're carrying — maybe they're going to a barbecue..."

"Those moves were developed by a master who was being attacked by bees at the time..."

Martial 'Art'

"Best technique to use? Try begging for mercy."

"Wait! There's a typo in these belt tying instructions!"

"Either get into a better defensive stance than that or I'll go rob someone who will!"

"I know karate. I can take care of myself in any situation..."

Martial 'Art'

"You have to use your hand to break the board. You can't use your opponent..."

"We don't want to break this hold!"

"Just call me 'BRUISE' Lee"

"Just like we did in class last night. I'll disarm him first, then I'll let you..."

Martial 'Art'

"Today we're going to cover walking and chewing gum!"

"I'm taking karate to save my teeth!"

"Next time close the windows before you have the students walk around blindfolded..."

"Boy, did you get the 'CHIP' knocked out of you...:

Martial 'Art'

"Where's that section on the proper way to dispute a call?"

"On the bright side, he's a doctor. So if he hurts you, he can cure you!"

"Lesson ten – how to defend against a gun"

"Our mascot has eaten judges that gave our team bad scores..."

Martial 'Art'

"He's taping a flashlight to his glove — says it's the only way you'll see it coming..."

"Today we'll cover refolding maps!"

"Wow! They really protect their quarterback!"

"Depending on how the class goes, some will be giving blood, some will be getting."

Martial 'Art'

"You're going to a halloween karate party as a board?"

"Those herbs cure hunger, it's my lunch!"

"Could you tell my kids there are secret moves hidden in housework?"

"I don't know, but I think the saying - what's in a name - might have some value here..."

Martial 'Art'

"Don't shake hands with him, he knows Judo!"

"Try that again and I'll shoot your kneecap off!"

"How are they going to teach us to walk softly way out here?"

"Let's dress as robbers and terrorize people, then they'll join our school to learn protection!"

Martial 'Art'

"We spend more time untangling them than scoring them!"

"Could you hold the gun in your other hand? I don't know how to defend from that side yet!"

"You've used that sleeper move on me so many times I decided to start wearing pajamas!"

Sparring Tournament Today

"I haven't fought yet. I accidently cut into the food line and bought the last piece of pizza..."

"Don't be silly, we'll be happy to show you that move again."

"He does 'roo' ryu and they tend to kick a lot..."

Martial 'Art'

"I only did what the hat said!"

"I want a bo staff, nunchaku, sai..."

"Let go! He's probably just as scared of you!"

"You kidding? I'm making a fortune!"

Martial 'Art'

"Hey! we found some people interested in taking karate!"

"There's nothing in the rules about wearing a snake for a belt..."

"Actually, karate is easy....it's keeping the pants up that's the hard part!"

"I love snake sparring! One punch and they usually knock each other out!"

Martial 'Art'

"Of course for better control you have to use smaller students..."

"With all the safety rules for sparring, this is all we can do now!"

"After I yank on the rope, you start kicking."

"Okay you're right, a squirting flower can be used for defensive purposes..."

Martial 'Art'

"Is that going to count against my score?"

"I figure i'm going to end up here so I might as well start here!"

"Before you attack, let me stretch out first."

"With this you'll never be in a situation without the right weapon at your disposal..."

Martial 'Art'

"Let me show you how to hold that knife – I study karate!"

"Rules are simple. You beat him, you eat him. He beats you, he eats you..."

"I'm not wearing a belled collar so the weapons class can hunt me in the dark!"

"Karate masters always appeared calm because they didn't have traffic jams to contend with!"

Martial 'Art'

"Will you hurry up and learn this technique before he kills me!"

"I don't care it's Valentine's Day! We throw punches, not kisses!"

Martial 'Art'

"Don't wave your hands while you're talking."

"Anybody attacks me with weapons, I don't plan on defending. I plan on running!"

Martial 'Art'

"You can't use computer mice tied together for nunchaku!"

"They want to spar to see who gets to control the TV remote tonight."

Martial 'Art'

"Spectator seats are wired for shock. So, you got something to say about my last call?"

"No, if you get into a fight you don't have to take your shoes off first..."

Martial 'Art'

"I don't like these new sparring uniforms!"

"Hey, when the going gets tough, I switch sides!"